My Fur Baby

Name: _____

Published by Hinkler Books Pty Ltd
45–55 Fairchild Street
Heatherton Victoria 3202 Australia
www.hinkler.com

hinkler

Authors: Zoe Antony and Sam Kiley
Cover design: Hinkler Design Studio
Internal design: Lisa Howard
Prepress: Splitting Image

ISBN: 978 1 4889 3428 5

Printed and bound in China

CONTENTS

My Pawfect Pooch's Profile

My perfect new name

....

Other potential names

....

....

....

Why my name was chosen

....

....

....

My breed

....

Known family or rescue origin

....

Age when I became part of
the family

....

The camera loves me!

My personality
(sum me up in 5 words!)

....

....

....

....

Introverted or extroverted?

....

When I'm happy, I...

....

....

....

....

....

....

When I'm cranky, I...

....

....

....

....

....

*A dog has the soul
of a philosopher.*
PLATO

The colour of my eyes

....

What is my fur like?
(long/short)

....

The colour of my fur

....

This is a lock of my fur

My birthday

....

My star sign

....

Important Information About Me

Microchip number

....

Council registration number

....

Council registration
records/renewals

....

....

....

....

....

....

....

Allergies

....

....

....

Emergency contacts
(family and friend connections)

....

....

....

....

....

Remember:
- use non-toxic ink
- be gentle with your
  dog's paw
- immediately wash
  off the ink with
  warm, dog-friendly
  soapy water

My first paw print

DID YOU KNOW?

33 per cent of dog
owners admit to having
talked to their dog over
the telephone, often
leaving them messages
on the answering
machine.

My Public Profile

Our Instagram/Facebook/
Twitter account/s

....

....

....

How many followers I have

....

My picture that has the most likes

My profile pics

My Family and Friends

My owner

....

....

....

Other family members

....

....

....

My family and friends

Our first home

....

....

....

Home, sweet home

8

My other pet brothers or sisters

....

....

....

....

Other people and pets I'm friends with

....

....

....

....

My First Days

We first met on (date)

....

At this location

....

....

....

What was special about me

....

....

....

....

....

My first reaction to my new home

....

....

....

....

....

....

I'm finally here!

After a couple of hours, I...

....

....

....

....

....

....

At the end of my first week, I...

....

....

....

....

....

What happened on my first night

....

....

....

....

....

....

....

Happiness is a warm puppy.
CHARLES M. SCHULZ

A memorable moment from our first week!

OUR FIRSTS

My first meal

....

....

Yum!

The first time I went to the bathroom outside

....

....

So proud!

My first walk

....

....

So excited!

First time I fell asleep on/next to my owner

....

....

Zzzz!

First time I wagged my tail

....

....

First time I barked

....

....

First time I socialised with
other dogs

....

....

....

My first journey in the car or
on public transport

....

....

....

My first trip to the vet

....

....

....

....

My first time I did something
on command

....

....

....

....

....

Woof!

My Favourite Things

My favourite foods

....
....
....
....

My favourite places to be patted

Circle on the diagram

My favourite place to sleep

....
....

Here's me busy chasing Zs

My favourite toys

....
....
....
....

My favourite games

....
....
....
....

Here's me with my toy babies

Here's me being cheeky

My favourite places to walk and sniff

....
....
....
....

No one appreciates the very special genius of your conversation as the dog does.
CHRISTOPHER MORLEY

Here's me being sneaky

OUR TYPICAL DAY

This is our typical day

....

....

....

....

....

....

....

....

We wake up at............................o'clock

Have breakfast at......................o'clock

Go for walks at.....................................

....o'clock

Have together time at.............o'clock

This is where I take my nap

We play together at..............o'clock

We have dinner at..............o'clock

We go to bed at..............o'clock

Activity time!

Dinner time!

Time for bed

DID YOU KNOW?
since their domestication, dogs have evolved to be able to read facial expressions, communicate jealousy, display empathy and even watch TV!

WHO'S A GOOD DOGGIE?

This is me learning to

Stay

Come

Do these tricks

Be toilet-trained

Be a good dog

DID YOU KNOW?

A typical dog has the same brain aptitude level as a toddler. Dogs can comprehend about 250 words and count up to five.

WALKIES!

My favourite time/s to walk

....

....

My favourite places to walk

....

....

....

I like to sniff and explore

....

....

....

....

Here's me adventuring!

My walking/park pals

....

....

....

....

....

My favourite games to play

....

....

....

....

....

Look at me go!

Here's me with my friends

OUR FIRST PUPPAVERSARY!

What we did to celebrate our puppaversary

....
....
....
....
....

Our best moment from the past year

....
....
....
....
....

What we learnt in the past year

....
....
....
....

Our first puppaversary pic

A dog is the only thing on earth that loves you more than he loves himself.

JOSH BILLINGS

Developments and highlights from the past year

....
....
....
....
....
....
....
....
....
....
....
....
....
....
....
....
....
....
....
....
....
....

GETTING UP TO MISCHIEF

Here's me being naughty in style!

Examples could include:

- Paw prints everywhere...

- Chewing shoes, furniture or people

- Raiding the bin for snacks

- Rolling in everything smelly

- Disinterest in or playing with food

The greatest pleasure of a dog is that you may make a
fool of yourself with him, and not only will he not scold
you, but he will make a fool of himself, too.

SAMUEL BUTLER

25

OUR BIG ADVENTURES!

Our notable travels, outings and adventures include

....

....

....

....

....

....

....

....

....

....

....

....

....

CANINE FEELINGS

I am a complex dog.
This is me when I am...

Sad

Happy

Grumpy

Playful

Angry

Excited

DID YOU KNOW?
Your dog can pick up on subtle changes in your scent, which can help him or her figure out how you are feeling — i.e. by smelling your perspiration when you become nervous or fearful.

THIRD PUPPAVERSARY

What we did to celebrate our puppaversary

....
....
....
....
....

Our best moment from the past two years

....
....
....
....
....

What we learnt in the past two years

....
....
....
....
....

Our puppaversary pic

DID YOU KNOW?
Studies indicate that petting your dog can lower your blood pressure.

Our highlights from the past two years

....
....
....
....
....
....
....
....
....
....
....
....
....
....
....
....
....
....
....
....
....
....
....

DOGGY DRESS-UPS

Two of my favourite costumes or pup accessories...

Two of my least favourite costumes or pup accessories...

33

FIFTH PUPPAVERSARY

What we did to celebrate our puppaversary

....
....
....
....
....

Our best moment from the past two years

....
....
....
....
....

What we learnt in the past two years

....
....
....
....
....

Our puppaversary pic

My little old dog — a heart-beat at my feet

EDITH WHARTON

Our highlights from the past two years

....
....
....
....
....
....
....
....
....
....
....
....
....
....
....
....
....
....
....
....
....
....

MY GROWN-UP DOGGO

How my tastes have changed over the years

....
....
....
....
....
....
....
....
....
....
....
....
....
....
....

So mature!

My favourite pastime is

....

....

....

....

....

How my personality has changed

....

....

....

....

....

Dogs are not our whole life, but they make our lives whole.

ROGER CARAS

Special snaps!

LET'S CELEBRATE!

This is how we celebrate special occasions

....

....

....

....

....

....

....

....

....

....

....

....

....

....

....

....

....

*Dogs and angels are
not very far apart.*
CHARLES BUKOWSKI

MY GROWTH

Date	Age	Length	Height	Weight

My evolution!

TOP TIP!

Finding and maintaining your dog's ideal weight can significantly extend your fur baby's life by almost 2 years! Their ideal weight varies from breed to breed, so ask your vet, but if your dog is the ideal weight you should be able to easily feel their ribs and be able to see their waist when viewed from the side and from above.

VACCINATIONS AND TREATMENTS

This should include core vaccinations, like the canine distemper vaccine, and non-core vaccines, like for canine parainfluenza (which can cause kennel cough).

Vaccination Type	Due By	Appointment On

Treatment (worming, flea control, etc.)	Due By	Medications

TOP TIP!

One of the best preventive health steps you can take for your doggie is to maintain their dental health. According to a recent study, 78 per cent of dogs over the age of three suffer from some form of dental disease, making it the most common health problem affecting dogs. It can also lead to a range of other serious health problems. One way to help is to make sure your pooch regularly has edible or medium-sized raw bones to chew on – this will help clean and keep their teeth strong as well as make them happy! Check in with your vet about the suitable type of bones or other treatments suited specifically to your pooch's requirements.

VISITS TO THE VET

Date	Reason	Treatment	Notes

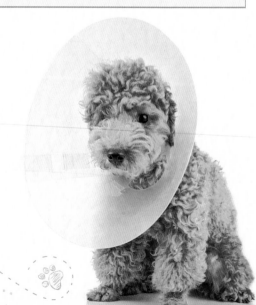

Date	Reason	Treatment	Notes

TOP TIP!

A trip to the vet can cause a lot of anxiety for you and your pooch! Ways to comfort your dog include bringing a familiar toy, a blanket and their most special treats to reward them. The best way to ward off anxiety is to make frequent trips to the vet for benign tasks, like weighing your dog, and then reward your fur baby so that they will start to have positive associations with the clinic.

THE PAWFECT TEAM

Me and you together (furever)!

Aaaaaawwwww!

A house is not a home until it has a dog.
GERALD DURRELL

Dog Milestone Cards

Use these cards to mark important moments in your fur baby's life. Simply cut out the card you want to use, place it beside your dog and take a photo! You can use some of these cards multiple times, especially the puppaversary card, which has room to write what puppaversary you're celebrating.

My First Day At Home

My First Day at the Park

Our Puppaversary

My First Walk

It's Playtime!

My First Obedience Lesson

My First Bath

Being 100% Adorable